Folk ... d

Sea Witch

SPHERE BOOKS LIMITED
London and Sydney

Kirk was a farmer and his land began at the foot of the mountain in the east and rolled over the fields and across streams until it tumbled over the cliffs to the sea. Kirk was alone but never lonely. There were those in the village who said it was high time he took a wife and many a hopeful mother sent her daughter with a freshly made loaf or home-made pie.

"Just something small for the young master with no one to look after him."

If Kirk understood these actions, he did not show it and each evening found him wandering over the darkening beach with his faithful sheepdog, Mac.

Kirk had always loved the sea. It was a part of

3

him. He knew the secret meanings of its every whim: its harsh relentless pounding waves in winter, its soft lulling, lapping in summer. He loved it most at the end of the day when the last light fell into its depths to sleep until dawn. He loved to watch the moonbeams skittishly glittering in its ripples and the bold moonlight turning it to silver.

Mac, too, found the beach exciting. Mac was all sheepdog, from the tip of his tail to the tip of his cold inquisitive nose. Mac could coax and bully a frightened sheep up the cliff to safety. Mac could scold a stubborn ewe reluctant to take shelter in a storm. Mac could find the smallest lamb buried under drifting snow. It seemed to Kirk that Mac

also took care of him. It was Mac who led the way home from the beach, found his master's slippers and slept at the foot of his bed.

It was Mac who first played with the seals. Mac chased everything that moved on the beach. He ran after the crab that side-stepped into its hiding place under a rock to take quick sly nips at Mac's nose and the gull that took off at the last moment to soar triumphantly skywards and then dive bomb the panting dog. He had learned to be wary of jelly fish when as a puppy he had stepped on one and had been stung.

The seals fascinated Mac. As they made their way awkwardly up the beach, Mac tried to hurry

them as though they were cumbersome sheep which had forgotten how to run and jump. He soon found that they were more fun in the sea. Their heavy bodies, so ponderous and clumsy on land became sleek, agile shafts of speed in the water, often playfully rolling Mac over. They out-swam and out-witted the dog but he did not mind. When Mac had had enough, he would bound up the beach and collapse in a wet, panting heap at Kirk's feet. Soon he would be up again, playing a one-sided game of tag with any seals on the beach or racing Kirk into the sea.

It seemed to Kirk that the seals spent more and more time on the beach. One seal, more

slender and agile than the others, often lingered at the water's edge after the others had disappeared. Sometimes this seal and Mac sat together but if Kirk approached, the seal slipped away.

One evening between dusk and night, when the soft light blends all colours into one hue so that all shapes fade into the background, Kirk felt strangely excited as he clambered down the rocky path to the beach. The sun had shone all day and he had stayed late in the fields. He had almost decided not to go to the beach but Mac had barked and pranced around and refused to come indoors.

As the cool sea breeze touched Kirk's face he

felt less tired. He breathed deeply and jumped the last few feet to the sand. He was surprised to see a group of seals still on a rock. They were gathered in a circle with one seal in the centre. Mac too seemed disturbed. He scampered ahead of Kirk towards the seals, slithering to a halt a few feet from them. He slid forward slowly on his belly, his whole body quivering. All the seals except one disappeared into the sea.

As Kirk watched, he saw Mac jump at the seal and to his horror, the seal's skin came away in the dog's mouth. At last Kirk reached the dog. The seal skin now lay on the sand and beside it, huddled in a wet brown cloak, was a young girl.

Quickly Kirk helped her to her feet. She was wet and shivering with cold. At first, the girl had difficulty in walking. She seemed to want to crawl on all fours and Kirk half carried, half dragged her across the beach. She managed the path more easily, using her hands and feet. Inside the house, she fell to the ground and pulled the wet cloak tightly around her. Kirk wrapped her in a warm thick blanket, and fed her spoonfuls of hot bread and milk. Soon she was asleep.

Kirk thought she was the most beautiful creature he had ever seen. Her brown silky hair tumbled in waves to her waist and her blue-grey eyes reminded Kirk of the sea. When she awoke in

the morning, she seemed puzzled by her surroundings and a little frightened. She did not speak, answering Kirk's questions with a smile and a nod. She seemed to know nothing of where she had been before Kirk found her on the beach.

He cleaned the spare room for her. Each morning Kirk and Mac set off for work leaving the girl behind. Her early clumsiness soon disappeared and Kirk thought her more beautiful each day. Kirk called her Ila.

Ila still spoke little but she often sang as she worked. Her voice was like the soft waves breaking gently over the sandy beach. Kirk could not understand her songs and sometimes her eyes

were sad, as if she were remembering things he knew nothing about.

She kept the little cottage spotlessly clean and there was always a meal ready when Mac and Kirk came home from work. She watched for them from the window and would run to meet them. Mac bounded ahead but Kirk did not hurry. Her beauty and grace as she ran with childlike eagerness towards him brought a lump to his throat. Mac adored her at once and soon Kirk loved her too. He claimed that she had put a spell on him and teasingly called her his Sea Witch.

They were married in the little church on the cliff top. Soon Kirk could not remember a time

without Ila and he thought she was happy too.

Ila liked to work in the fields with Kirk. She liked it best when it was raining and the wind blew strong from the sea. She would stand, head held high until she was soaked to the skin. She would sing and dance and never seemed to feel the cold.

Ila was happiest in the sea. Whenever possible she slipped away to the beach. She swam so fast that Kirk could not keep up with her. Sometimes she swam out so far that Kirk feared she would not come back. Then Ila would lie on the beach or chase Mac. She would never stay in the sea or on the beach if there were any seals about. Kirk noticed at such times she would return to the

cottage and shut the door and all the windows.

The villagers were suspicious and a little afraid of Ila. No one knew where she had come from and some said she had magical powers. It was whispered that she had cured the cobbler's wife's headache and the blacksmith's daughter of a fever.

Late one night there was a knock on the crofter's door. Outside was a young woman whom Kirk recognised as the daughter of a wealthy merchant in the village. In her arms was a small baby.

"He can't breathe," she cried.

Gently Kirk took the baby from her and handed the wee bairn to his wife.

Ila felt the baby's forehead which was dry and hot. He breathed with shallow rasping gasps and his little hands fluttered helplessly.

"There is no time to lose," said Ila. "Hold the baby Kirk while I get some medicine for him."

Quickly Ila selected some seaweeds that she kept hanging in the kitchen. She pounded them to a powder and poured boiling water on to the mixture. The mother watched anxiously as Ila held the baby so that he breathed the steamy vapour that rose from the bowl. Gradually the child's breathing eased, the trembling hands stilled and soon he was sleeping peacefully.

Gently Ila handed the baby back to his

mother.

"He will sleep until morning and then he will be alright," she said quietly. The mother whispered thank you but Ila would not accept any payment.

"If you ever need help," said the baby's mother, "please come to me."

After this Ila was always welcome in the village and everyone was happy when a little girl was born to Kirk and Ila. The baby was named Fiona and to Kirk's delight grew more and more like her mother everyday. She had the same gentle smile and quiet ways, the same grey-blue eyes.

Ila took the baby to the beach when she was a few days old. Fiona loved the water and could

swim before she could walk. Mac followed her everywhere, sleeping by her cot at night and barking at anyone who came too close to her.

One night, with Fiona tucked in her cot and the table laid for supper, Kirk became aware of a strong wind blowing from the sea. The fire was stoked with peat and the firelight cast flickering shadows over the white-washed walls. Gently then more insistently, the wind howled around the house and rattled the shutters. Suddenly three shots were heard. A ship was in distress out in the bay.

Leaving Mac to guard Fiona, Kirk and Ila ran out of the cottage and hurried along the cliff top.

A thick swirling, twisting mist had smothered the warning beam from the lighthouse. A ship had drifted too close to the rocks and would soon break up. All on board would be drowned.

The wind was much stronger outside and Kirk and Ila clung to each other and fought the wind together. The gale lifted the waves high against the cliffs and spray tasted salty on their lips. There had been shipwrecks before.

In a few minutes the mist lifted and Kirk could see the ship. She lay on her side with the waves crashing over her deck. The sails were torn and pulled apart by the wind. Around her floated trunks and cargo that had been jettisoned to lighten

the ship in an effort to refloat her. People clung to the rigging and to each other. Fathers held their children and mothers frantically clutched their babies. As Kirk watched, the ship heaved and two men were thrown into the churning sea. Then the ship settled even deeper into the water. The mist swirled and Kirk could see no more.

Kirk could hear people clambering over the beach below. Rescuers were trying to fire a line to the ship but their efforts were useless. They could only guess the position of the ship and the wind caught the line and threw it back. All the time the waves pounded the ship. People on the beach came together, silent, heads bowed in prayer for the souls

they knew would soon be lost. When the wind blew towards the shore, the creaking of the ship and the cries for help could be heard.

Several of the strongest men waded out with the rescue line but the sea was too rough and they were forced back. One was so battered and weakened that he had to be dragged from the water.

"I have never known the sea to be so rough," gasped one. "No one could survive in that."

A woman wept quietly and turned away.

"It's the Northern Star," said Kirk. "There are fifty people on board, and all will be drowned."

Again and again they tried to fire the rescue line. Suddenly Ila left Kirk and scrambled down the

cliff path. She grasped the line, tied it around her slender waist and ran into the sea. Desperately Kirk called to her but if she heard she took no heed and soon Kirk could not see her. Silence fell on those watching on the beach. The preacher led the little group on the beach in a prayer for her.

Then from the ship came the signal that the line had been secured. Soon the hawser was in place and the first of the victims pulled to safety. They all spoke of the young girl who had climbed on to the ship. One man spoke also of the seals that swam alongside her and seemed to be guiding her. Her courage had calmed everyone. When all but the Captain had been rescued, she had jumped

overboard to swim back to the shore.

Frantically, Kirk searched the water's edge. The storm had subsided and the sea was now still. Pathetic relics of the night drifted in; the ship's log, its saturated pages showing no trace of the disaster, trunks and cases broken open with their contents torn and lost, a broken doll, a woman's shoe. Then as the first light of a new day crept over the horizon, the mist lifted and Kirk saw Ila lying motionless in the sand. She was so still that he thought she was dead. Joyfully he realized that she was breathing. Gently he lifted her and carried her home.

The ship could now be seen clearly. Her back had been broken in two and the sea would soon

39

break her into little pieces. All day the villagers ferried to and from the boat salvaging as much as they could for the survivors.

The village hall had been turned into a shelter for the people rescued from the ship. Some were so shocked they could not believe they were alive. Because of Ila, not one life had been lost.

Ila said little about the rescue but Kirk could see a new sadness in her smile, a longing in her eyes that he did not understand. She no longer wanted to work with him in the fields. Even Mac was sad. Ila spent more and more time on the beach. Kirk would find her sitting, pale and motionless on the sands looking out to sea, her face so sad that he

knew that he would soon lose her. Each time she swam so far out to sea that he could not see her, he thought that this time had come.

The only time Ila smiled was when she was with Fiona. The little girl had grown quickly. She could swim nearly as well as her mother but did not always follow her into the water. She would wait patiently, guarded by Mac, for her mother to swim back to them.

One day Kirk found Fiona alone on the beach and he knew that he would not see his beloved Ila again. Holding his little daughter close, he searched the sea shore until darkness fell. Fiona fell asleep and sadly he carried her home. Mac refused to leave

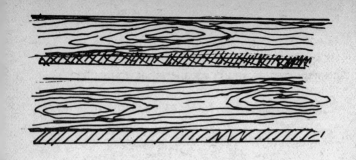

and wandered up and down the beach whimpering

for his mistress.

Kirk put Fiona to bed then, reluctantly,

climbed the little wooden stairs to the loft. Slowly

he opened the chest in which he had placed a seal

skin that had lain beside Ila so many years ago. He

felt inside the empty chest but as he feared the skin

had gone. He knew Ila had returned to her true

home. For a long time he sat in the loft recalling the

happy times they had shared together, remembering

her kindness and her courage. He knew that he

would love her forever. Fiona cried in her sleep.

Quickly Kirk left the loft. Picking her up he

comforted her and sang quietly to her as Ila had

and soon the child was quiet.

Each evening Kirk and Fiona and Mac searched the sea. Sometimes when they saw a group of seals on the waters edge they would hurry towards them. Once a seal lingered on the beach when all the others had gone. Joyously, Mac ran towards the creature. In the half light, Kirk knew it was Ila and he called her name. But as he approached, the seal slipped into the water.

*   *   *   *

The years passed and Fiona grew up and had a family of her own. One evening Kirk kissed Fiona and held her close as he had done so often when she was a little girl, went out in his boat with Mac and did not come back.

The seals still come ashore and the people are glad to see them. They will tell you that as long as the seals are there, there will never be shipwrecks along this stretch of coastline again.

Illustrations by John Fane

© C.E.S.
First Published 1979
Published in this edition by Sphere Books Ltd 1985
30–32 Gray's Inn Road, London WC1X 8JL

Printed and bound in Great Britain by
Cox & Wyman Ltd, Reading